INSIDE II  DE OUT

CHORD SONGBOOK

WITHDRAWN

WITHDRAWN

PUBLISHED BY
WISE PUBLICATIONS
14-15 BERNERS STREET, LONDON, W1T 3LJ, UK.

EXCLUSIVE DISTRIBUTORS:
MUSIC SALES LIMITED
DISTRIBUTION CENTRE, NEWMARKET ROAD,
BURY ST EDMUNDS, SUFFOLK, IP33 3YB, UK.

MUSIC SALES PTY LIMITED
120 ROTHSCHILD AVENUE, ROSEBERY,
NSW 2018, AUSTRALIA.

ORDER NO. AM988416
ISBN 13: 978-1-84609-838-3
ISBN 10: 1-84609-838-6
THIS BOOK © COPYRIGHT 2006 WISE PUBLICATIONS,
A DIVISION OF MUSIC SALES LIMITED.

EDITED BY TOM FARNCOMBE.
MUSIC ARRANGED BY DAVID WESTON.
MUSIC PROCESSED BY PAUL EWERS MUSIC DESIGN.

PRINTED IN THE EU.

WWW.MUSICSALES.COM

YOUR GUARANTEE OF QUALITY:
AS PUBLISHERS, WE STRIVE TO PRODUCE EVERY BOOK
TO THE HIGHEST COMMERCIAL STANDARDS.

THE BOOK HAS BEEN CAREFULLY DESIGNED TO
MINIMISE AWKWARD PAGE TURNS AND TO MAKE
PLAYING FROM IT A REAL PLEASURE.
PARTICULAR CARE HAS BEEN GIVEN TO SPECIFYING
ACID-FREE, NEUTRAL-SIZED PAPER MADE FROM PULPS
WHICH HAVE NOT BEEN ELEMENTAL CHLORINE BLEACHED.

THIS PULP IS FROM FARMED SUSTAINABLE FORESTS
AND WAS PRODUCED WITH SPECIAL REGARD FOR
THE ENVIRONMENT.

THROUGHOUT, THE PRINTING AND BINDING HAVE
BEEN PLANNED TO ENSURE A STURDY, ATTRACTIVE
PUBLICATION WHICH SHOULD GIVE YEARS OF ENJOYMENT.

IF YOUR COPY FAILS TO MEET OUR HIGH STANDARDS,
PLEASE INFORM US AND WE WILL GLADLY REPLACE IT.

INSIDE IN THE INSIDE OUT
KOOKS
CHORD
SONGBOOK

WISE PUBLICATIONS
part of The Music Sales Group

London/NewYork/Paris/Sydney/Copenhagen/Berlin/Madrid/Tokyo

THE KOOKS
DISCOGRAPHY

ALBUM: **Inside In/Inside Out**
(23/01/2006)
Virgin CDV3016

Seaside/See The World/Sofa Song/
Eddie's Gun/Ooh La/You Don't Love Me/
She Moves In Her Own Way/Matchbox/
Naïve/I Want You/If Only/Jackie Big Tits/
Time Awaits/Got No Love

SINGLES: **Eddie's Gun**
(11/07/2005)
7" (VS2000): Eddie's Gun/California/
Bus Song

Sofa Song
(17/10/2005)

7" (VS1904): Sofa Song/Something To Say

CD (VSCDT1904): Sofa Song/Be Mine

DVD (VSDVD1904): Sofa Song/Eddie's Gun/
Put Your Back To My Face

You Don't Love Me
(09/01/2006)

7" (VS1910): You Don't Love Me/Lonely Cat

CD 1 (VSCD1910): You Don't Love Me/
Slave To The Game

CD2 (VSCDX1910): You Don't Love Me
(Live At The Garage)/See The World
(Acoustic - Live At Abbey Road)/
The Window Song/You Don't Love Me (Video)/
See The World (Video)

Naïve
(27/03/2006)

7" (VS1911): Naïve/Tea and Biscuits

CD (VSCDT1911): Naïve/Hiding Low

CD 2 (VSCDX1911): Naïve/I Love That Girl/Naïve (Demo)/Naïve (Video)/ You Don't Love Me (Live Video)

She Moves In Her Own Way
(26/06/2006)

7" (VS1913): She Moves In Her Own Way/ I Already Miss You

CD 1 (VSCDT1913): She Moves In Her Own Way/Do You Love Me Still?

CD 2 (VSCDX1913): She Moves In Her Own Way (Radio Version)/In My Opinion/ Give In/She Moves In Her Own Way (Video)

Ooh La
(23/10/2006)

7" (VS1918): Ooh La/Ask Me

CD 1 (VSCDT1918): Ooh La/Sofa Song (Alternative Version)

CD 2 (VSCDX1918): Ooh La/I Don't Mind/ Matchbox (Live)/Ooh La (Video)

Compilations with other artists:

Radio 1 Live Lounge
(16-10-2006)
CD (BMG 82876833092): Crazy

ASK ME

Words & Music by
Luke Pritchard, Hugh Harris, Max Rafferty & Paul Garred

E   A   Asus⁴   A*

Esus⁴   C♯m   A**   G♯m⁷   A***

Tune guitar down a semitone

Intro   ‖: E   :‖ *Play 9 times*

Verse 1

A   Asus⁴ A*
And I see you there,

                    E   Esus⁴ | E |
Trying to take that load.

A⁶   Asus⁴   A*
And I'm now so much   strong - er

                    E   Esus⁴ | E |
Than I ever gave you cre - dit for.

C♯m   A** G♯m⁷
And it's so much better if you ask me,

A***   E | E Esus⁴ | E   ‖
If you just went along to the par - ty.

Verse 2

A   Asus⁴ A*
And I see you there,

                    E   Esus⁴   E
Trying to take that load, but it's not your load.

C♯m   A** G♯m⁷
And I think it's so much better in the end,

A***   E
'Cause you're really driving me round the bend.

Outro | E Esus⁴ | E | E |

             | E | E | E   ‖

BE MINE

Words & Music by
Luke Pritchard, Hugh Harris, Max Rafferty & Paul Garred

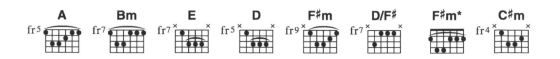

A	Bm	E	D	F#m	D/F#	F#m*	C#m
fr5	fr7	fr7	fr5	fr9	fr7		fr4

Intro | A | Bm | E | A |

| D | Bm | F#m E A | A ‖

Verse 1
  (A) Bm   E
I never thought we'd come this far,
      A   D Bm
But then how come that far.
         F#m E   A
And I won't let   them in.
              F#m   E   A
'Cause she's my lover and not my friend.

Verse 2
  (A) Bm   E
I'm so scared to lose you now,
      A   D Bm
So easy to lose you now.
           F#m   E   A
Because there calling at my door.
         F#m   E   A
So I'm locking up my door.

Verse 3
  (A)   Bm   E
Now my thoughts are very dark,
      A   D Bm
And my dreams are always dark.
         F#m E   A
Don't let them take me a - way,
       F#m E   A
'Cause I want me to stay.

Chorus 1

| A D/F#| A   D/F#

But be mine, oh.

        A   D   E

Won't you be mine, oh.

   Bm   D/F#

Be mine, oh oh.

F#m* D   Bm |E |

Take it all out - side

C#m   D

  'Cause you don't need it

Bm   E

Don't need to cry, oh no

F#m* D   Bm |D   E |

Take it all out - side

F#m*   D

'Cause you don't need me

Bm   D E

Don't need to   cry.

Link 1 | A | A   ‖

Verse 4   As Verse 1

Verse 5

(A) Bm   E

I'm so scared to lose you now,

        A   D   Bm

Oh it's so easy to lose you now.

             F#m E   A

Because there calling at my door.

         F#m   E   A

So I'm locking up my door.

Chorus 2

```
 | A  D/F# |        A       D/F#
                Oh be mine, oh.

                        A       D/F#
          Won't you be mine, oh.

             Bm       D      E
          Be mine, be mine.

          F#m*  D       Bm    | E          |
          Take it all out - side

          C#m                    D
            'Cause you don't need it

          Bm              E
          Don't need to cry, oh no

          F#m*  D       Bm    | D   E   |
          Take it all out - side

          F#m*               D
          'Cause you don't need me

          Bm            D  E
          Don't need to cry,   yeah.
```

Outro

```
 | F#m   E    A  | (A)              |
                   So be mine.
 | F#m   E    A  | (A)              |
                   Oh be mine.
 | F#m   E    A  | (A)              |
                   Oh be
 | F#m   E    A  | (A)             ||
              mine.
```

BUS SONG

Words & Music by
Luke Pritchard, Hugh Harris, Max Rafferty & Paul Garred

Intro

| A | B | A | E B |

| A | B | A | E B ||

(w/vocals ad lib)

Verse 1

    E   B   F♯m7
You know today I stayed on the bus,

        C♯m   D   A* E* G D* A
Oh yeah, I waited and waited until I was at your stop.

    E   B   F♯m7
The driver said to me "Just don't make a fuss"

           C♯m   D   A* E* G D* A
And I said "In the end you've taken all my money, my friend."

Chorus 1

F♯m   B   G♯m7   C♯m7 Cm7   F♯m
But ow ow, yes you love it as I take you on when you down,

       B   G♯m7   C♯m7 Cm7 F♯m
And ow ow, something happened and now I can't sing a - long.

       B   G♯m7   C♯m7 Cm7   F♯m
And ow ow, yes you hate it as I try to get under your skin,

       B   G♯m7   C♯m7 Cm7 A
And ow ow, something happened and now you can't sing a - long.

Link

As Intro

Verse 2

```
      E                B        F#m7
         But you know today I stayed on the train,
            C#m                  D                   A*  E*   G D* A
      Oh yes, I waited and waited until I could not re - frain.
      E                B        F#m7
      The driver said to me "Just don't make a fuss like you did on the bus"
            C#m                         D                        A*   E*  G D* A
      In the end you've taken all my money, you're not my friend.
```

Chorus 2

```
      F#m   B          G#m7       C#m7  Cm7         F#m
      But ow ow, yes you love it as you take me on when I'm down,
            B          G#m7              C#m7 Cm7  F#m
      And ow ow, something happened and now I can't sing a - long.
            B          G#m7       C#m7     Cm7      F#m
      And ow ow, yes you love it as you try to get under my skin.
            B     | A* E* G D* | A   E   ‖
      And ow ow.
```

CALIFORNIA

Words & Music by
Marlon Jennings

| D* | Bm* | D | Bm |
| G | G5 | G5/F♯ | A | Em |

Intro　　| D* | Bm* | D* | Bm* ‖

Verse 1

D　　　　　　　　　　　　Bm
Don't you know baby, I'm a leading man.
　　G
I dig down deep when I say I love you.
D　　　　　　　　　　　　　Bm
Well I can hold my own with the best of them,
　　G
I guarantee you, you never seen nothing,
G5　　　　　　G5/F♯　D
Nothin' like this a - gain.

Chorus 1

(D)
California say that you love me,

From all the darkness I couldn't break through.
　　　　　　　　　　　Bm　　　　D　　A
Now, I miss the o - cean when I go to sleep,
　Bm　　　　　Em　　　D
Oh man, it's gonna break my heart.

Link 1　　| D | Bm | D | Bm ‖

Verse 2

D   Bm
Don't you know that I did the things I did.

  G
I rubbed your back when you were sleeping.

D   Bm
But all along baby it was understood,

    G
That you were leaving, absolutely,

   G5   G5/F♯   D
The very first day we met.

Chorus 2

(D)
California say that you miss me,

From all the darkness I couldn't break through.

(D)   Bm
I'm gonna miss you.

               D
I'm gonna miss you.

               Bm
I'm gonna miss you.

Link 2   ‖: D | Bm | D | Bm :‖

Outro

D
I'm gonna miss ya.

Bm
I'm gonna miss you.

D
I'm gonna miss ya.

Bm
I'm gonna miss you.

| D | Bm |

D   Bm
I'm gonna miss you.

‖: D* | Bm* | D* | Bm* :‖ *Repeat to fade w/vocal ad libs.*

CRAZY

Words & Music by
Thomas Callaway, Brian Burton, Gianfranco Reverberi & Gian Piero Reverberi
(This arrangement by The Kooks)

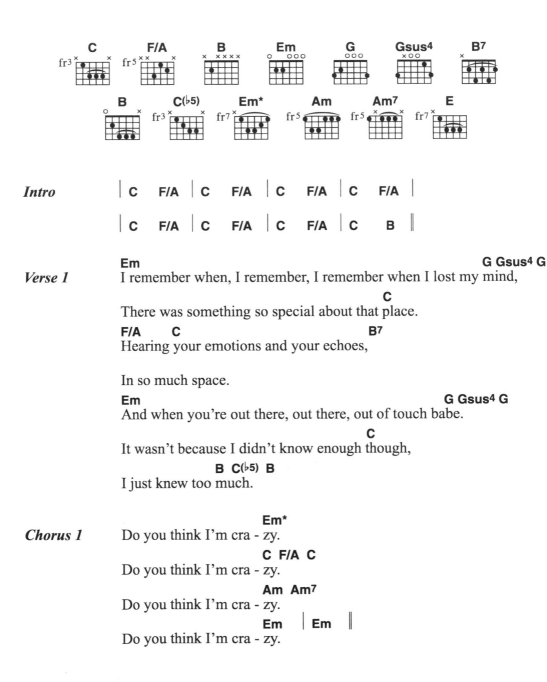

Intro

| C F/A | C F/A | C F/A | C F/A |

| C F/A | C F/A | C F/A | C B |

Verse 1

Em   G Gsus⁴ G

I remember when, I remember, I remember when I lost my mind,

                                               C

There was something so special about that place.

F/A   C   B⁷

Hearing your emotions and your echoes,

In so much space.

Em   G Gsus⁴ G

And when you're out there, out there, out of touch babe.

                                           C

It wasn't because I didn't know enough though,

                 B C(♭5) B

I just knew too much.

Chorus 1

                        Em*

Do you think I'm cra - zy.

                        C F/A C

Do you think I'm cra - zy.

                        Am Am⁷

Do you think I'm cra - zy.

                        Em | Em ‖

Do you think I'm cra - zy.

Bridge 1

  E   **C F/A C**
I hope that you are having the time of your life.
                    E   **C**   **C F/A C**
Don't think twice, don't think twice, that's my ad - vice to you babe.

Verse 2

Em
Come on now, who do you, who do you, who do you,
                     G Gsus4 G
who do you think you are.
                  C   F/A C
Ha ha ha bless your soul,
                         B B(♭9) B
You really think you're in con - trol.

Chorus 2

                       Em*
Yeah, I think you're cra - zy
          G Gsus4 G
I think you're cra - zy
          C F/A C
Oh, I think you're cra - zy
          B7   │ **B7**   ‖
I think you're cra - zy baby.

Bridge 2

  E   **C F/A C**
My heroes had the heart to live how I would like to live.
        E   **C F/A C**
And all I remember is thinking, I want to be like them.

Chorus 3

(C)   **B**   **Em**
Do you think I'm cra - zy.
                    G Gsus4 G
Do you think I'm cra - zy.
                    C
Do you think I'm cra - zy.
Am   **Em**
  Do you think I'm cra - zy child.

DO YOU LOVE ME STILL?

Words & Music by
Luke Pritchard & Hugh Harris

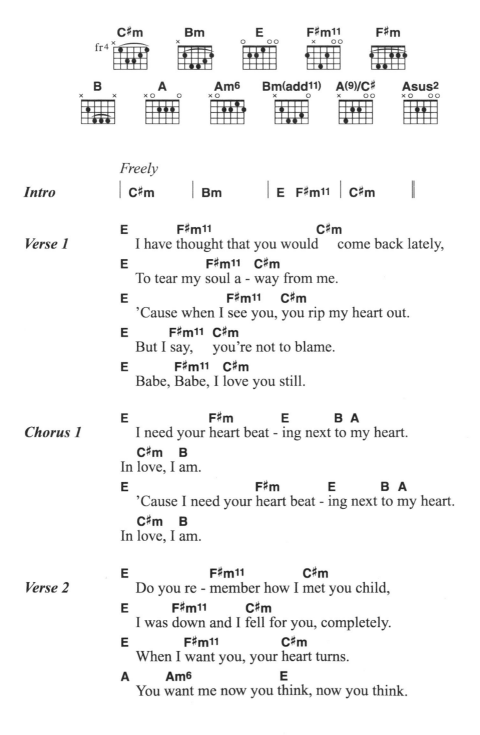

Freely

Intro | C#m | Bm | E F#m11 | C#m ‖

Verse 1
    E   F#m11   C#m
I have thought that you would   come back lately,
    E   F#m11 C#m
To tear my soul a - way from me.
    E   F#m11 C#m
'Cause when I see you, you rip my heart out.
    E   F#m11 C#m
But I say,   you're not to blame.
    E   F#m11 C#m
Babe, Babe, I love you still.

Chorus 1
    E   F#m   E   B A
I need your heart beat - ing next to my heart.
C#m B
In love, I am.
    E   F#m   E   B A
'Cause I need your heart beat - ing next to my heart.
C#m B
In love, I am.

Verse 2
    E   F#m11   C#m
Do you re - member how I met you child,
    E   F#m11   C#m
I was down and I fell for you, completely.
    E   F#m11   C#m
When I want you, your heart turns.
    A   Am6   E
You want me now you think, now you think.

Chorus 2

      E   F♯m   E   B A
I need your heart beat - ing next to my heart.

     C♯m   B
In love, I am.

      E   F♯m   E B   A
'Cause I need your heart danc - ing next to my heart.

     C♯m   B
In love, I am.

Link 1   ‖: Bm(add11) A(9)/C♯ | Asus2 | Bm(add11) A(9)/C♯ | Asus2   :‖

Outro

    | E F♯m11 | C♯m   B
                       Babe, do you love me still?

    | E F♯m11 | C♯m
                   'Cause I miss you.

     E F♯m11   C♯m
      I miss you babe.

      A   Am6 | E   ‖
I, I miss you.

EDDIE'S GUN

Words & Music by
Luke Pritchard, Hugh Harris, Max Rafferty & Paul Garred

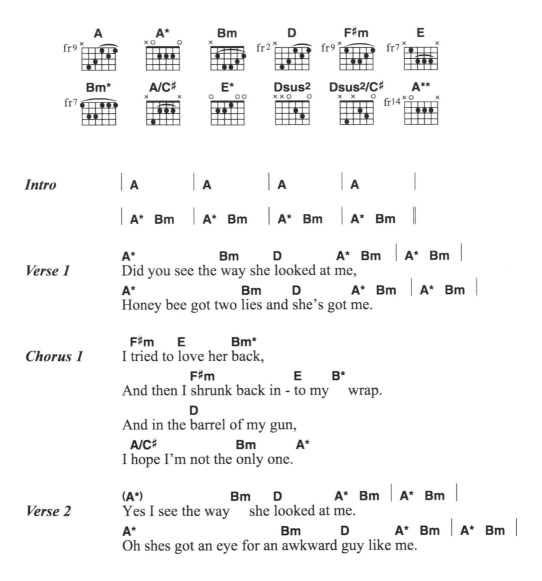

Intro

| A | A | A | A |

| A* Bm | A* Bm | A* Bm | A* Bm ‖

Verse 1

A*   Bm D   A* Bm | A* Bm |
Did you see the way she looked at me,

A*   Bm D A* Bm | A* Bm |
Honey bee got two lies and she's got me.

Chorus 1

F♯m E Bm*
I tried to love her back,

    F♯m   E B*
And then I shrunk back in - to my wrap.

     D
And in the barrel of my gun,

 A/C♯   Bm A*
I hope I'm not the only one.

Verse 2

(A*)   Bm D   A* Bm | A* Bm |
Yes I see the way she looked at me.

A*   Bm   D A* Bm | A* Bm |
Oh shes got an eye for an awkward guy like me.

Chorus 2

        F♯m   **E** **Bm***
I tried to love her back,

              F♯m   **E**   **B***
And then I shrunk back in - to my wrap.

              D
And in the barrel of my gun,

  A/C♯   **Bm**   **A***
I hope I'm not the only one.

              D
And in the barrel of my gun,

  A/C♯   **Bm A*** | **A*** |
I hope I'm not the only one.

Link 1 | **A** | **A**   ‖
                        Yeah!

Bridge | **E*** | **Bm** | **F♯m*** | **A*** |
                Do do do do do do do.   Do do do

         | **E*** | **(E*)** | **Dsus2 Dsus2/C♯**| **Bm**   ‖
         do do.

Chorus 3   As Chorus 2

Outro

        A   **A***
Adah, adah,   adah, adah, adah, oh

        D   **A/C♯**
I tried to love her back,

        A*
And then I shrunk back in - to my wrap.

             D
And then I tried to love,

   A/C♯   **A*** | **A***   ‖
I tried to love her back.

GOT NO LOVE

Words & Music by
Luke Pritchard, Hugh Harris, Max Rafferty & Paul Garred

G   C5   Em   D   C   A   Em7

Intro | Drums | Drums | (G) | (G) | G   C5 | G   C5 ‖

Verse 1

     G   C5   G
     You,

               C5 | G   C5 | G   C5 ‖
     You ain't got no love to - day.

Verse 2

     G   C5   G
     You,

               C5 | G   C5 | G   C5 ‖
     You ain't got no love to - day.

Chorus 1

     Em   D   C   G | G   ‖
       And don't let them bring you down.

Verse 3   As Verse 2

Chorus 2   As Chorus 1

Bridge

     Em   A   G   D   C
     And hold on, don't let them   bring you down.

     Em   A   G   D   C
     And hold on, don't let them   bring you down.

Interlude	G C5	G C5	G C5	G C5
	Em7 D C	G C5	G ‖	

Chorus 3

Em   D   C   G | G   ‖
And don't let them bring you down.

Em   D   C   G | G   ‖
And don't let them bring me down.

(G)

Outro
w/vocal ad lib.

Got no, got no. Got no, got no, got no love.

Got no, got no, got no love. Oh, ooh. Ooh, oh oh.

Oh, ooh, oh. Whoa, ooh.

HIDING LOW

Words & Music by
Luke Pritchard, Max Rafferty, Paul Garred & Peter Denton

D   A/C#   Bm   A   G   F#m

Intro

D A/C#	Bm A/C#	D A/C#	A
G	A	Bm A	G
A	F#m	G	Bm A
G	G A ‖

Verse 1

D   A/C# Bm A/C# D A/C# A
Hid - ing low, low   with - out you.

   G   A
The world can be so cal - lous,

   Bm A   G
Tell me what should we do?

       A   F#m
Should we play on each other

   G   Bm
Life ends, in the end

A G A
Life ends.

Verse 2

D   A/C♯   Bm   A/C♯
   So gabble slow, now

D   A/C♯ A
She told me of her   eyes.

   G   A
But bleed with me brother,

         Bm   A   G
Like we're friends till the end.

        A   F♯m
And I'll put on my eyeshades

      G   Bm
Like it, in the end

A   G   A
Life ends.

Link 1

| D   A/C♯| Bm A/C♯| D   A/C♯| A |

| G | A | F♯m | G | G   ‖

Outro

(G)   Bm A
In the end,

     G | G |
Life   ends.

       Bm A G | A | D   ‖
In the end, my life ends.

GIVE IN

Words & Music by
Luke Pritchard

Intro

| Dm | Am/C G | G   C | G/B F | F Dm ||

Verse 1

(Dm) Am/C G   C   G/B   F   F(#11)
I   want you,   and you want me

Dm   Am/C   G   C   G/B   F
And there's nothing stopping you   from kissing me.

Dm   Am/C   G   C   G/B   F
So I'm tearing my hair out,   because I want you.

Chorus 1

Dm   Am/C   G F   Dm
Give in to your heart, and don't let him sell you out.

                         Am/C   G F   Dm
Give in to your heart, I won't let you be so down.

Link

As Intro

Verse 2

(Dm) Am/C G   C   G/B   F
I   need you,   do you still want me?

Dm   Am/C   G   C   G/B   F
There's nothing stopping us,   from touching each other

Dm   Am/C   G   C   G/B   F
Are you tearing your hair out?   'Cause I already have been.

Chorus 2

Dm   Am/C   G   F
Give in to your heart and don't let your life before it's over.

Dm   Am/C   G   F   G
Give in to your heart and don't let him sell you out.

F   G | G | G |
Him sell you out.

G   G/F   Em
Give in, give in, give in to me.

I DON'T MIND

Words & Music by
Paul Garred

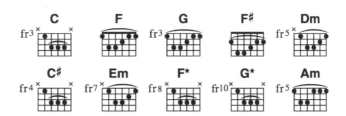

Verse 1

  C   F   G | G   F# |
Give it a chance and let them know,

  F   Dm C
I never want to hurt you so.

  (C)   F   G | G   F# |
I never seem to hold your hand

  F   Dm C
I just want to un - der - stand.

  C# Dm   Em F* G*
I don't mind. I don't mind.

       Am   G   C
It's how I feel. How I feel. Oh oh.

Verse 2

  C   F   G | G   F# |
Give it a chance to let them know,

  F   Dm C
I never want to hurt you so.

  (C) Dm   Em F* G*
I don't mind. I don't mind

       Am   G
It's how I feel. How I feel.

       Am   C   F* Dm C
How I feel. How I f - e - e - l.

I ALREADY MISS YOU

Words & Music by
Luke Pritchard

D   D/C♯   Bm   Dsus4   A   G   A/C♯

Capo fourth fret

Intro
| D | D   D/C♯ ‖

Verse 1

Bm   D   Dsus4 D
I know you're feeling bitter,

A   G   D   Dsus4 D
What I said last I didn't mean.

Bm   D   Dsus4 D
And now that I'm a little better,

A   G   D
This is what I meant to say.

Chorus 1

D   A
Babe, I al - ready miss you.

          D   A   G
Sweet - heart I al - ready miss you.

          D   A   G
Sweet - eyes I al - ready miss you.

A   G   D   A/C♯
And you only just walked out the door.

Link 1
| Bm   A/C♯ | D   ‖

Verse 2

Em   **G**
You know I hate talking on telephones,

D   **C**   **G**
I'm so sorry it's just my way.

Em   **G**
And now that I'm a little older,

D   **C**   **G**
So much to you I'd like to say.

Chorus 2

G   **D**
Babe I al - ready miss you.

G   **D**   **C**
Sweetheart I al - ready miss you.

       G   **D**   **C**
Sweet - eyes I al - ready miss you.

D   **C**   **G**
And you only just walked out the door.

I LOVE THAT GIRL

Words & Music by
Luke Pritchard, Max Rafferty, Paul Garred & Peter Denton

E5   A7   Bm   A   E7

Intro   ‖: E5 | E5 | E5 | E5 :‖   *Play 3 times*

Verse 1

E5
I got off the train this evening to see my baby,

My baby's she's blue, but not as blue as me.
        A7
'Cause I love that girl, yes I love that girl,
            E5
But she's with another man tonight.
        Bm
But she, she treat me so bad
A   E5
She kicked me out of our house, our house.

Verse 2

(E5)
Now listen, I like this girl and she treats me fine,

But I don't speak to her like she's my kind of girl.
A7
But if things are to give the girl back
    E5
I think Yeah-o.
        Bm
But I, I need that girl now 'cause she
A   E5
Understands me and no one else does.

Link 1   As Intro

                             A7   **E5**

Verse 3   But I love that girl, yes I love that girl, I do.

                                    Bm   **E5**

Oh, but she treats me, treats me so, treats me so, treats me so, bad.

Oh its all my fault anyway.

Link 2   ‖: **E5** | **E5** | **E5** | **E5**   :‖

                (E5)

Bridge   I wanna swagger like Jagger when he moves in a room.

w/vocal ad libs   **A7**

throughout   Let me just see her and tell her how I feel,

                E5

I'm just a bad boy.

                  Bm

Oh I need that girl,

                A   **E7**

I've stitched myself up al - ready.

I WANT YOU

Words & Music by
Luke Pritchard, Hugh Harris, Max Rafferty & Paul Garred

Dm   Bm   B♭sus2   D5   B♭5   F

B♭   B♭/F   C   G   B♭maj7   B♭maj7/F

Intro
| N.C. | N.C. | |
| Dm | Bm | Dm | B♭sus2 ‖

Verse 1
D5   B♭5   F   B♭   B♭/F
Take me back to the place where I loved that girl for all time.
           D5   B♭5   F   B♭   B♭/F
And why must life just take away every good thing, one at a time.

Chorus 1
    B♭
I want you back, oh yes I want it back.
       C   Dm
Oh yes I want you back, please give it me back.
           B♭
'Cause I want your love.

Verse 2
D5   B♭5   F   B♭   B♭/F
How can I not even cry, for such a big thing in my life.
           D5   B♭5   F   B♭   B♭/F
The pain it takes the heart of me. Turn around and say goodbye.

Chorus 2
    B♭
I want you back, oh yes I want it back.
       C   Dm
Oh yes I want you back, please give it me back.
       B♭
'Cause I want you.

Bridge

Dm
How did you do it females?

C
'Cause always you do it angels,

G | B♭maj⁷ B♭maj⁷/F |
You always keep me on the run.

Dm
So how did you do it angels?

C
And always you do it females,

G | B♭maj⁷ B♭maj⁷/F |
You always keep me on the run.

Interlude   ‖: Dm | Bm | Dm | Bm :‖

Chorus 3

B♭
I want it back, oh yes I want it back.

C   Dm
Oh yes I want you back, please give it me back.

B♭
'Cause I want your love.

But I can't let myself love you.

Outro | B♭ | B♭ | B♭ | B♭ | B♭ ‖

IF ONLY

Words & Music by
Luke Pritchard, Hugh Harris, Max Rafferty & Paul Garred

Bm Bsus2 Bm7 F#sus4 D

Em7 F#m7 Dmaj7 Bm7* D*

Intro | Bm | Bm | Bsus2 | Bsus2 ||

Verse 1

Bm   N.C.
   So hold your head and hold your tongue.

But only say what you have to.
Bm7   F#sus4   D
   And as a child, yes I dreamed
         Em7   Bm7
Of holding her   in the silver screen.
         F#sus4
She loved her man, and loved him twice.
D   Em7
   I wish I'd been   that passenger.
Bm7   F#sus4   D
   Having fun, flying my kite.
         Em7   Bm7
The devil inside won't control my life.

Pre-chorus 1

(Bm7)   F#sus4   D
Too much love, so little hate.
         Em7   F#m7   Em7
The devil in - side won't con - trol my fate.

Chorus 1

(Em7) Dmaj7   Em7 Dmaj7
   Oh, if only, if only. Oh, he wasn't so lonely
Em7   Dmaj7   Em7
   He'd have someone to play with,
   Dmaj7
In - stead of bombing our neighbours.

| *Link 1* | ‖ Bm7* | F♯m7 | D* | Em7 ‖ |

Verse 2

Bm7   F♯sus4   D
So here I go,   to see the world
       Em7
With my eyes and with my soul.

Pre-chorus 2   As Pre-chorus 1

Chorus 2   As Chorus 1

Link 2

| ‖ (Dmaj7) | Dmaj7 | Dmaj7 | Dmaj7 |

| ‖ Bm7 | F♯sus4 | D | Em7 ‖ |

Verse 3

Bm7 N.C.
So   hold your head and run my time.
                       Bm7
The what of life, no man can hide.
          F♯sus4   D
And here we are, and here we bleed.
     Em7   Bm7
To be a victim, there's no need.
      F♯sus4
Having fun, I never fight.
D   Em7   Bm7
The devil in - side controls my life.

Pre-chorus 3   As Pre-chorus 1

Chorus 3

(Em7) Dmaj7   Em7 Dmaj7
Oh, if only, if only. Oh, he wasn't so lonely
Em7   Dmaj7   Em7
He'd have someone to play with.
   Dmaj7   Em7
In - stead of bombing our neighbours.
Dmaj7   Em7 Dmaj7
Oh, if only, if only. Oh, he wasn't so lonely
Em7   Dmaj7   Em7
He'd have someone to play with,
D*
Instead of bombing our neighbours.

IN MY OPINION

Words & Music by
Luke Pritchard, Hugh Harris, Max Rafferty & Paul Garred

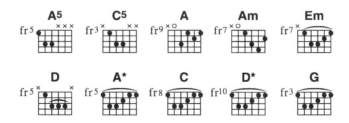

Intro | N.C. | A5 A5 D C♯ A C5 C5 G A G E | Em D ‖

Verse 1

w/riff 1 *(x4)*
Only I can find a little piece of my mind,

Take you out and we'd sit beneath the moon of what I think.

Inside of you, I do see you would love to be free,

So take it now its your right, there's no need to fight.

Chorus 1

A   Am   Em   D
Take a piece of my heart for you,   take a piece of my love for her.
A   Am   Em   D
Take a piece of my heart for him,   take a piece of my soul.
Em   C   D*   A*
    I tried once again to get my opinion up in their minds,
         G   Em   C
Their just far too blind taking all of me
                       D*
And put it in the bottom of the sea if they were right.

Link 1 ‖: riff 1 | (riff 1) :‖

Verse 2

w/riff 1 *(x4)*
If only you could find a little piece of your time,

I'd take you to a club where they strip, oh don't bite those sweet lips.

Inside of you I do see, I know I know you don't want me to,

Oh 'cause everything's shooting up shooting up more than it seems.

Chorus 2

A   **Am**   **Em**   **D**
Take a piece of my love for her,   take a piece of my soul for him.
A   **Am**   **Em**   **D**
Take a piece of my heart for you,   take a piece of my soul.
Em   **C**   **D***   **A***
  I tried once a - gain to get my o - pinions in their minds,
         G   **Em**
They just don't have mine.
           C   **D**
Want my wish, my life, as they sold by my side,
w/riff 1 *(x2)*
Shadow stain - suddenly stays.

JACKIE BIG TITS

Words & Music by
Luke Pritchard, Hugh Harris, Max Rafferty & Paul Garred

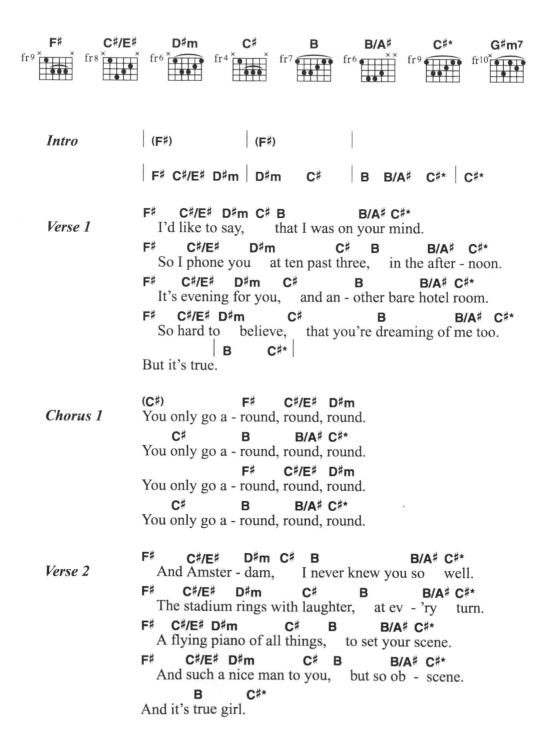

Intro | (F♯) | (F♯) |

| F♯ C♯/E♯ D♯m | D♯m C♯ | B B/A♯ C♯* | C♯* ‖

Verse 1

F♯   C♯/E♯ D♯m C♯ B   B/A♯ C♯*
I'd like to say,   that I was on your mind.

F♯   C♯/E♯   D♯m   C♯   B   B/A♯ C♯*
So I phone you   at ten past three,   in the after - noon.

F♯   C♯/E♯ D♯m C♯   B   B/A♯ C♯*
It's evening for you,   and an - other bare hotel room.

F♯   C♯/E♯ D♯m   C♯   B   B/A♯ C♯*
So hard to   believe,   that you're dreaming of me too.
            | B   C♯* |
But it's true.

Chorus 1

(C♯)   F♯   C♯/E♯ D♯m
You only go a - round, round, round.

        C♯   B   B/A♯ C♯*
You only go a - round, round, round.

                F♯   C♯/E♯ D♯m
You only go a - round, round, round.

        C♯   B   B/A♯ C♯*
You only go a - round, round, round.

Verse 2

F♯   C♯/E♯   D♯m C♯ B   B/A♯ C♯*
And Amster - dam,   I never knew you so   well.

F♯   C♯/E♯   D♯m   C♯   B   B/A♯ C♯*
The stadium rings with laughter,   at ev - 'ry   turn.

F♯ C♯/E♯ D♯m   C♯   B   B/A♯ C♯*
A flying piano of all things,   to set your scene.

F♯   C♯/E♯ D♯m   C♯   B   B/A♯ C♯*
And such a nice man to you,   but so ob - scene.

        B   C♯*
And it's true girl.

```
                     (C♯)              F♯     C♯/E♯  D♯m
Chorus 2      You only go a - round, round, round
                        C♯        B        B/A♯  C♯*
              You only go a - round, round, round
                              F♯     C♯/E♯  D♯m
              You only go a - round, round, round
                        C♯        B        B/A♯  C♯*
              You only go a - round, round, round


                     (B)          C♯*            F♯      C♯/E♯    D♯m     C♯
Bridge           And Jack - ie Big Tits, is   hid - ing in the corner.
                 B       B/A♯  C♯*                  G♯m7   F♯  C♯/E♯
                 Respect    is the word she shouts,    as I im - plore her.
                 B                C♯*
                 And speaks her mind not me,
                     F♯            C♯/E♯    D♯m   C♯
                 For   I was only speaking freely.
                 B          B/A♯  C♯*
                 And in - terupt me once more,
                         G♯m7     F♯     C♯/E♯
                 And I'll take you to the cleaners.


                                      F♯     C♯/E♯  D♯m
Chorus 3      You can't push me a - round, round, round.
                        C♯           B        B/A♯  C♯*
              You can't push me a - round, round, round.
                              F♯     C♯/E♯  D♯m
              You only go a - round, round, round.
                        C♯        B     B/A♯  C♯*
              You only go a - round,    round, round.
              B
              And Jackie Big Tits.
```

LONELY CAT

Words & Music by
Luke Pritchard

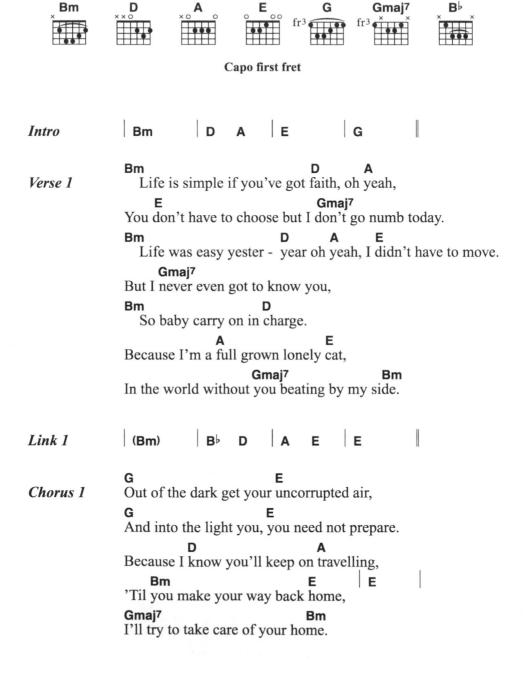

Capo first fret

Intro | Bm | D A | E | G |

Verse 1

Bm   D   A
Life is simple if you've got faith, oh yeah,
    E   Gmaj7
You don't have to choose but I don't go numb today.
Bm   D   A   E
Life was easy yester - year oh yeah, I didn't have to move.
        Gmaj7
But I never even got to know you,
Bm   D
   So baby carry on in charge.
                 A   E
Because I'm a full grown lonely cat,
                    Gmaj7   Bm
In the world without you beating by my side.

Link 1 | (Bm) | B♭ D | A E | E |

Chorus 1

G   E
Out of the dark get your uncorrupted air,
G   E
And into the light you, you need not prepare.
               D   A
Because I know you'll keep on travelling,
   Bm   E | E |
'Til you make your way back home,
Gmaj7   Bm
I'll try to take care of your home.

Link 2   As Intro

Verse 2

Bm   **D**   **A**   **E**
Patch my life up with Sello - tape oh yeah, it doesn't feel so safe,
          Gmaj⁷
But all the   same I don't have to choose.
Bm   **D**   **A**   **E**
How sad baby is that, yeah I'm a full grown lonely   cat,
                   Gmaj⁷   **Bm**
In the world without you beating by my side.

Link 3 | (Bm) | B♭ D | A E | E G ‖

Chorus 2

G   **E**
And out of the dark get you uncorrupted air,
G   **E**
And into the light you, you need not prepare.
            D   **A**
Because I know you'll keep on travelling,
        Bm   **E**
Till you find your way back home,
        Gmaj⁷   **Bm**
I'll try to take care of your home.

Outro | (Bm) | D A | E | G   ‖

MATCHBOX

Words & Music by
Luke Pritchard, Hugh Harris, Max Rafferty & Paul Garred

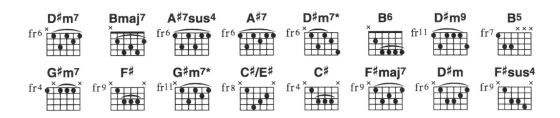

Intro | N.C. |: D#m7 Bmaj7 | A#7sus4 A#7 |

| D#m7* B6 | A#7sus4 A#7 :|

Verse 1
D#m9   A#7sus4   A#7
Viciously she sleeps, and walks along her lonely beat.
    D#m7*   B6   A#7sus4   A#7
She trips, falls into it all. And I wish I bite my lip
         D#m7 Bmaj7 A#7sus4 A#7   D#m7*
And call her a - way,   from you my little one.
B6   A#7sus4   A#7
  Oh, you my little one.

Bridge 1
D#m7   B5   G#m7
    Don't come too close, you don't wanna see my ghost.
D#m7   B5   G#m7
  Your turn but I'm betrayed by you my sweetheart.
D#m7   B5
  And don't you think that you went too far?
         G#m7
And do you want to see my heart bleed?
D#m7   B5   N.C.
  For you, you and him, him and you. You know my heart bleeds.

Chorus 1

D#m7   F#   G#m7*
And all of us, we're going out tonight.
            F#   C#/E#   D#m7
We're gonna walk all over your cars.
            F#   G#m7*
The Kooks are out in the street.
              F#   C#/E#   D#m7
Oh, were gonna steal your skies.
        F#   G#m7*
All of us, we're going out tonight.
            F#   C#/E#   D#m7
We're gonna walk all over your cars.
            F#   G#m7*
The Kooks are out,   in the street.
             F#   C#/E#
Oh we're gonna steal your...

Verse 2

    F#   C#   F#   C#
I'm sorry   that I let you go.
  F#   C#   F#   C#
I let you down, I let you down my dear.
    F#   G#m7*   F#   G#m7*
I al - ways seem to play these games   with you my dear.
  F#   G#m7*   F#   G#m7*
I always, so, so, so, always. So.

Chorus 2

D#m7   F#   G#m7*
And all of us, we're going out tonight.
            F#   C#/E#   D#m7
We're gonna walk all over your cars.
            F#   G#m7*
The Kooks are out in the street.
              F#   C#/E#   D#m7
Oh, were gonna steal your skies.
        F#   G#m7*
All of us, we're going out tonight.
            F#   C#/E#   D#m7
We're gonna walk all over your cars.
            F#   G#m7*
The Kooks are out   in the street.
                 D#m7
Oh they're gonna steal your skies.

Link 1 | D♯m7 | F♯maj7 | D♯m | F♯ F♯sus4 F♯ ‖

D♯m   F♯   F♯sus4 F♯ D♯m   F♯   F♯sus4 F♯
Oh, oh, my Julia wh - oa. I'll never betray you my love.
D♯m   F♯   F♯sus4 F♯ D♯m   F♯
Oh, oh, my Julia wh - oa. I'll never betray you my love.

            D♯m7   F♯
Chorus 3   ‖:   And all of us, we're going out tonight.
w/vocal ad lib.   D♯m7
We're gonna walk all over your cars.

The Kooks are out in the street.

Oh, were gonna steal your skies. :‖
D♯m7 N.C.
Don't come too close, you don't wanna see my ghost.

Your turn but I'm betrayed by you my sweetheart.

NAÏVE

Words & Music by
Luke Pritchard, Hugh Harris, Max Rafferty & Paul Garred

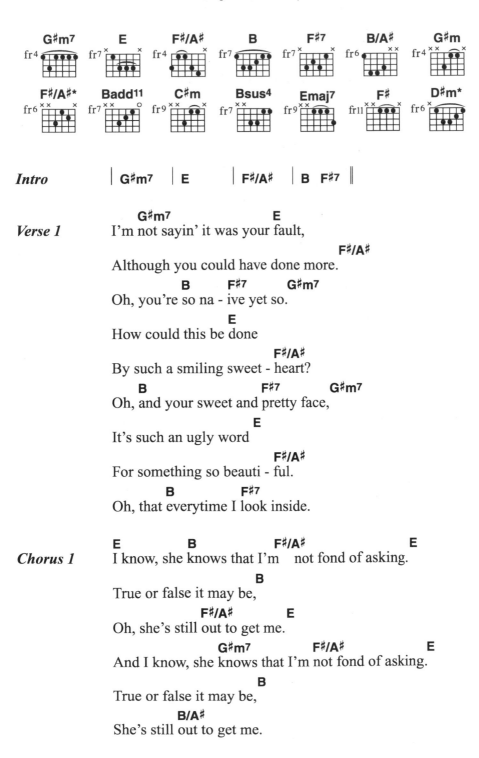

Intro | G#m7 | E | F#/A# | B F#7 ‖

Verse 1
G#m7   E
I'm not sayin' it was your fault,

F#/A#
Although you could have done more.

B   F#7   G#m7
Oh, you're so na - ive yet so.

E
How could this be done

F#/A#
By such a smiling sweet - heart?

B   F#7   G#m7
Oh, and your sweet and pretty face,

E
It's such an ugly word

F#/A#
For something so beauti - ful.

B   F#7
Oh, that everytime I look inside.

Chorus 1
E   B   F#/A#   E
I know, she knows that I'm   not fond of asking.

B
True or false it may be,

F#/A#   E
Oh, she's still out to get me.

G#m7   F#/A#   E
And I know, she knows that I'm not fond of asking.

B
True or false it may be,

B/A#
She's still out to get me.

| Link 1 | │ E   │ E   ‖ |

Verse 2

G♯m7   E
     I may say it was your fault,

                            F♯/A♯
Because I know you could have done more.
         B   F♯7   G♯m7
Oh you're so na - ive yet so.
                 E
How could this be done

                     F♯/A♯
By such a smiling sweet - heart?
      B   F♯7   G♯m7
Oh, and your sweet and pretty face,

It's such an ugly word
E   F♯/A♯
    For something so beauti - ful,
      B   F♯7
That everytime I look inside.

Chorus 2   As Chorus 1

Interlude   │ G♯m F♯/A♯* │ Badd11 C♯m │ Bsus4   │ Emaj7   │

                   │ G♯m F♯/A♯* │ Badd11 C♯m │ F♯   │ F♯   ‖

Verse 3

G♯m7   E
     So how could this be done

                     F♯/A♯
By such a smiling sweet - heart?
      B   F♯7   G♯m7
Oh you're so na - ive yet so.

Such an ugly thing
E   F♯/A♯
    For someone so beauti - ful,
      B   F♯7
But everytime you're on his side.

Chorus 3   As Chorus 1

Outro   E   D♯m*   G♯m7
                          B   E   D♯m*   G♯m7
                 Just don't let me down.
                          B
                 Just don't let me down

                 ‖: E   D♯m*   G♯m7
                    Hold on to your kite,
                          B   E   D♯m*   G♯m7
                 Just don't let me down.
                          B
                 Just don't let me down :‖

                 E   D♯m*   G♯m7
                 Hold on to this kite,
                          B   E   D♯m*   G♯m7
                 Just don't let me down.

                 Just don't let me down.

OOH LA

Words & Music by
Luke Pritchard, Hugh Harris, Max Rafferty & Paul Garred

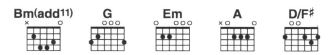

Tune guitar down a semitone

Intro
| Bm(add¹¹) | Bm(add¹¹) | Bm(add¹¹) ‖

Verse 1

       (Bm(add¹¹))   G
In their eyes is the place where you finally discover that you love it here.
                    Em
You've got to stay on this rock, not a rock, an island
                  Bm(add¹¹)
On which you found a lover.

Then you twitch, you felt that itch in you petty coat,
                Em
Your pretty pretty pettycoat.
            Bm(add¹¹)
And then you smiled, he got wild,
                          G
You didn't understand that there's money to be made.
                   Em   A | E   ‖
Beauty is a card that must get played by orga - nisations.

Chorus 1

Bm(add¹¹)   G   A   Em | Em D/F♯
   But ooh la,   she was such a good girl to me.
G   Bm(add¹¹)   A   A   D/F♯
   And ooh la,   the world just chewed her up, and spat her out.
G   Bm(add¹¹)   A   Em | Em D/F♯
   And ooh la,   she was such a good girl to me.
G   Bm(add¹¹)   A   Em
   And ooh la,   the world just chewed her up, and spat her out.

Link 1
| Bm(add¹¹) | Bm(add¹¹) | G | G |

| Em | Em | Bm(add¹¹) | Bm(add¹¹) ‖

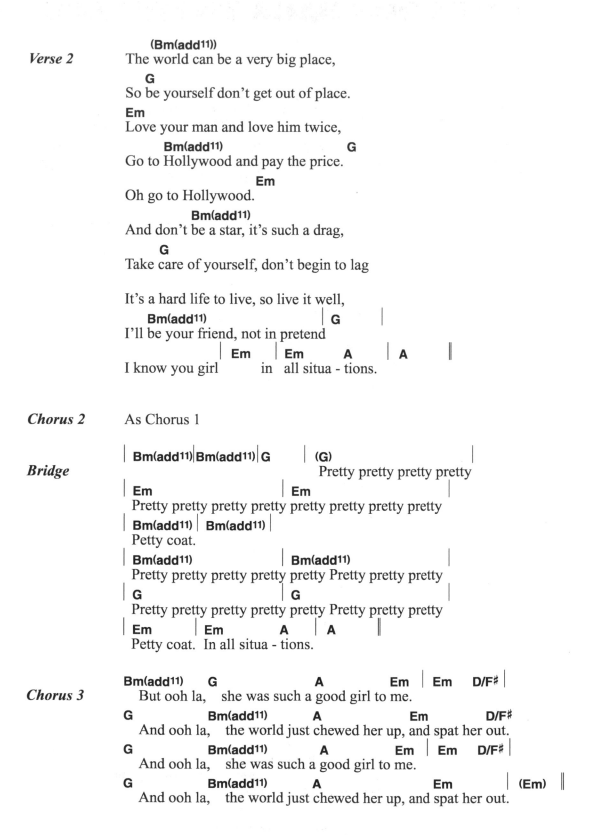

Verse 2

(Bm(add11))
The world can be a very big place,

  G
So be yourself don't get out of place.

Em
Love your man and love him twice,

   Bm(add11)   G
Go to Hollywood and pay the price.

          Em
Oh go to Hollywood.

     Bm(add11)
And don't be a star, it's such a drag,

 G
Take care of yourself, don't begin to lag

It's a hard life to live, so live it well,

  Bm(add11) | G
I'll be your friend, not in pretend

     | Em | Em   A | A
I know you girl   in all situa - tions.

Chorus 2   As Chorus 1

Bridge

| Bm(add11)| Bm(add11)| G | (G)
                   Pretty pretty pretty pretty

| Em | Em
Pretty pretty pretty pretty pretty pretty pretty pretty

| Bm(add11) | Bm(add11)
Petty coat.

| Bm(add11) | Bm(add11)
Pretty pretty pretty pretty pretty Pretty pretty pretty

| G | G
Pretty pretty pretty pretty pretty Pretty pretty pretty

| Em | Em   A | A
Petty coat. In all situa - tions.

Chorus 3

Bm(add11)   G   A   Em | Em   D/F#
  But ooh la, she was such a good girl to me.

G   Bm(add11)   A   Em   D/F#
  And ooh la, the world just chewed her up, and spat her out.

G   Bm(add11)   A   Em | Em   D/F#
  And ooh la, she was such a good girl to me.

G   Bm(add11)   A   Em | (Em)
  And ooh la, the world just chewed her up, and spat her out.

PUT YOUR BACK TO MY FACE

Words & Music by
Luke Pritchard, Hugh Harris, Max Rafferty & Paul Garred

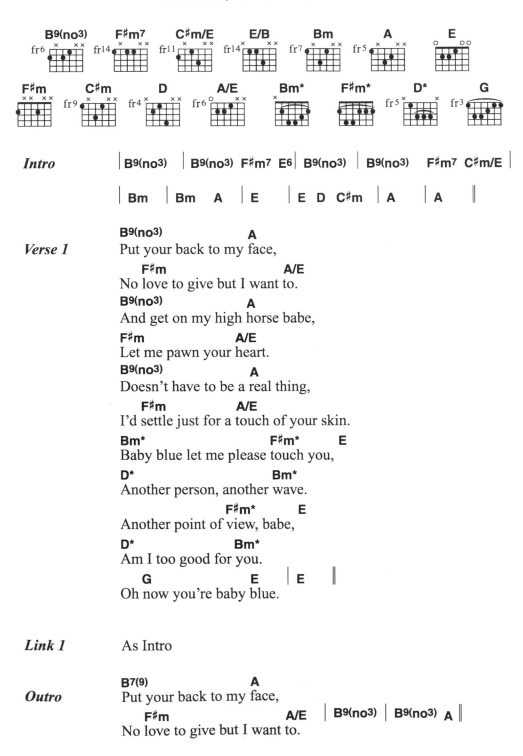

Intro | B9(no3) | B9(no3) F♯m7 E6 | B9(no3) | B9(no3) F♯m7 C♯m/E |

| Bm | Bm A | E | E D C♯m | A | A ‖

Verse 1

B9(no3)　　　　　　　A
Put your back to my face,

　F♯m　　　　　　　　A/E
No love to give but I want to.

B9(no3)　　　　　　A
And get on my high horse babe,

F♯m　　　　　　A/E
Let me pawn your heart.

B9(no3)　　　　　　　A
Doesn't have to be a real thing,

　F♯m　　　　　　A/E
I'd settle just for a touch of your skin.

Bm*　　　　　　　F♯m*　　　E
Baby blue let me please touch you,

D*　　　　　　　　Bm*
Another person, another wave.

　　　　　　　F♯m*　　　E
Another point of view, babe,

D*　　　　　　　Bm*
Am I too good for you.

　G　　　　　　　E | E ‖
Oh now you're baby blue.

Link 1　　As Intro

Outro

B7(9)　　　　　　　A
Put your back to my face,

　F♯m　　　　　　　　A/E | B9(no3) | B9(no3) A ‖
No love to give but I want to.

© Copyright 2005 Famous Music Publishing Limited.
All Rights Reserved. International Copyright Secured.

50

SEE THE WORLD

Words & Music by
Luke Pritchard, Hugh Harris, Max Rafferty & Paul Garred

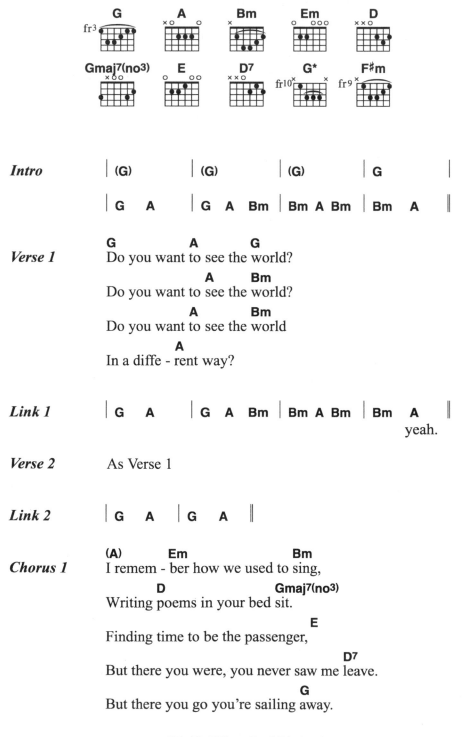

G fr3	**A**	**Bm**	**Em**	**D**
Gmaj7(no3)	**E**	**D7**	**G*** fr10	**F♯m** fr9

Intro | (G) | (G) | (G) | G |

                | G   A | G A Bm | Bm A Bm | Bm   A ‖

Verse 1
```
G            A        G
Do you want to see the world?
              A      Bm
Do you want to see the world?
              A      Bm
Do you want to see the world
              A
In a diffe - rent way?
```

Link 1 | G   A | G A Bm | Bm A Bm | Bm   A ‖

                                            yeah.

Verse 2   As Verse 1

Link 2 | G   A | G   A   ‖

Chorus 1
```
(A)      Em                 Bm
I remem - ber how we used to sing,
           D              Gmaj7(no3)
Writing poems in your bed sit.
                                E
Finding time to be the passenger,
                              D7
But there you were, you never saw me leave.
                           G
But there you go you're sailing away.
```

cont.

       Bm   **G**
And you know. You never come away,

            Bm   **G**
Yeah but you should. You never lie to me,

       Bm   **G**
Yeah but I will. You never come away,

       Bm
Yeah but you should.

Link 3 | **G** | **G**   **A** | **Bm** | **Bm** **A** ||

Verse 3

G   **A**   **G**
What do you real - ly want to see?

            A   **Bm**
What do you really want to see?

           A   **Bm**
What do you real - ly want to see

         A
On your tele - vision screen?

Link 4   As Link 2

Chorus 2

(A)   **Em**   **Bm**
I remem - ber how we used to be

              D   **Gmaj7(no3)**
Without the world upon our TV.

You let it lie or you can take it back,

E   **D7**
Or wrap your life around evil's track.

But there you are, you're sailing away.

           G   **Bm**
But there you are. And you know.

           G   **Bm**
You never come away, yeah but you should.

           G   **Bm**
You never lie to me, yeah but I will.

           G   **Bm**
You never come away, yeah but you should.

Link 5 | G* | F♯m Bm | G* | F♯m Bm ‖

                          G*   F♯m Bm

Outro   And do you want to see the world?

              G*
              What, what.

              F♯m   Bm   G* | F♯m Bm |
              And do you want to see the world?

              G*
              What what.

              F♯m   Bm
              And do you want to see the

              G*
              What, what what.

              F♯m   Bm   G*
              And do you want to see the world?

              F♯m Bm
              What, what, what.

              G*   F♯m Bm
              And do you want to see the   world?

              G*
              What, what, what.

              F♯m   Bm   G* | F♯m Bm |
              Yeah do you want to see the world?

              G*
              What, what, what.

              F♯m   Bm
              What do you really want to...

              G*
              What, what.

              F♯m   Bm
              What do you really want to...

              G*
              What, what.

              F♯m   Bm   G | F♯m Bm | G* | Bm   ‖
              What do you really want to see?

SEASIDE

Words & Music by
Luke Pritchard, Hugh Harris, Max Rafferty & Paul Garred

Dm **F** **B♭** **C** **G** **G/F** **Dm***

Capo first fret

Intro | Dm | Dm ‖

Verse 1
Dm   **F**
D' you want to go to the sea - side?
        B♭   **C**
I'm not   trying to say that everybody wants to go.
Dm   **F**
    I fell in love at the seaside,
        B♭   **C**
I handled my charm with time   and sleight of hand.

Link 1 | G | G | G | G G/F ‖

Verse 2
Dm   **F**
D' you want to go to the sea - side?
        B♭   **C**
I'm not   trying to say that everybody wants to go.
Dm   **F**
    I fell in love an the seaside
        B♭   **C**
She handled her charm with time   and sleight of hand,
| G | G | G | G G/F ‖
    land, lo.

Chorus 1

Dm   B♭
  But I'm just trying to love you

    C
Any kind of way.

Dm   B♭
  But I find it hard to love you girl,

            C | G | G | G | G G/F ‖
When you're far away,   away.

Verse 3

| Dm* | Dm* |

(Dm*)   F
D' you want to go to the sea - side?

    B♭   C   Dm*
I'm not trying to say that every - body wants to go.

            F   B♭
But I fell in love on the seaside,

      F   B♭
On the seaside,

    F
In the seaside.

SHE MOVES IN HER OWN WAY

Words & Music by
Luke Pritchard, Hugh Harris, Max Rafferty & Paul Garred

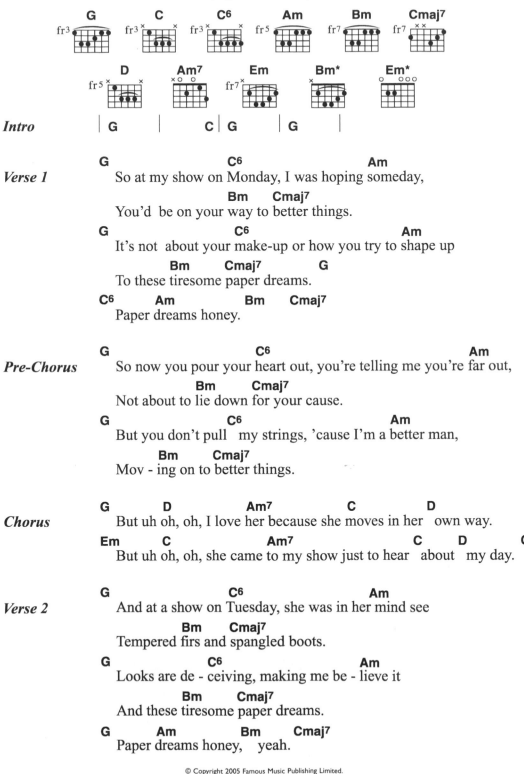

Intro

| G | | C | G | G | |

Verse 1

G   C6   Am
So at my show on Monday, I was hoping someday,
      Bm Cmaj7
You'd be on your way to better things.
G   C6   Am
It's not about your make-up or how you try to shape up
    Bm Cmaj7   G
To these tiresome paper dreams.
C6 Am   Bm Cmaj7
Paper dreams honey.

Pre-Chorus

G   C6   Am
So now you pour your heart out, you're telling me you're far out,
    Bm Cmaj7
Not about to lie down for your cause.
G   C6   Am
But you don't pull my strings, 'cause I'm a better man,
    Bm Cmaj7
Mov - ing on to better things.

Chorus

G D   Am7   C   D
But uh oh, oh, I love her because she moves in her own way.
Em C   Am7   C D G
But uh oh, oh, she came to my show just to hear about my day.

Verse 2

G   C6   Am
And at a show on Tuesday, she was in her mind see
    Bm Cmaj7
Tempered firs and spangled boots.
G   C6   Am
Looks are de - ceiving, making me be - lieve it
    Bm Cmaj7
And these tiresome paper dreams.
G Am   Bm Cmaj7
Paper dreams honey, yeah.

Pre-Chorus

G   C6   Am
So won't you go far, tell me you're a keeper,

                    Bm   Cmaj7
Not about to lie down for your cause.

G   C6   Am
But you don't pull my strings 'cause I'm a better man,

              Bm   Cmaj7
Mov - ing on to better things.

Chorus 2

G   D   Am7   C   D
But uh oh, oh, I love her because she moves in her own way.

Em   C   Am7   C   D   G
But uh oh, oh, she came to my show just to hear about my day.

Bridge

Em   D   Bm   C G
Yes I wish that we never made it through all the summers.

Em   D   Bm* C   G
And kept them up instead of kicking us   back down to the suburbs.

Solo

| Em* G |(G) | Am7   G|(G) |

| Em* G |(G) | Am7   G|(G) |

Chorus 3

G   D   Am7   C   D
But uh oh, I love her because she moves in her own way.

Em   C   Am7   C   D   G
But uh oh, she came to my show just to hear about my day.

              D   Am7   C   D
But uh oh, oh, I love her because she moves in her own way.

Em   C   Am7   C   D   G
But uh oh, oh, she came to my show just to hear about my day.

SLAVE TO THE GAME

Words & Music by
Luke Pritchard, Hugh Harris, Max Rafferty & Paul Garred

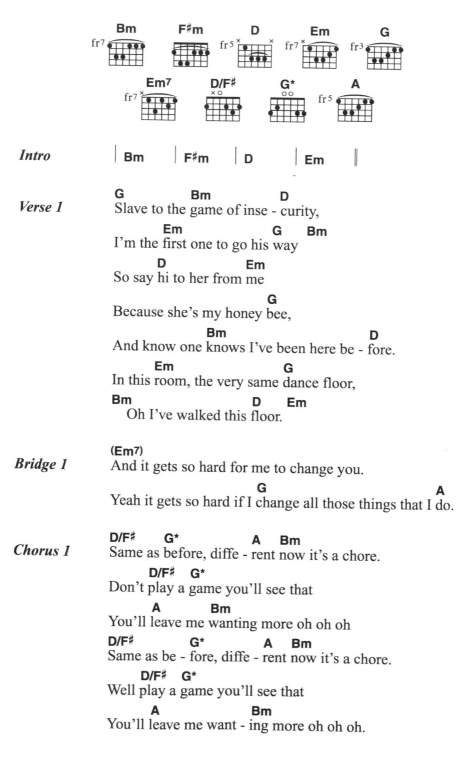

Intro

| Bm | F#m | D | Em ‖

Verse 1

G   Bm   D
Slave to the game of inse - curity,

         Em   G   Bm
I'm the first one to go his way

      D   Em
So say hi to her from me

                   G
Because she's my honey bee,

            Bm   D
And know one knows I've been here be - fore.

     Em   G
In this room, the very same dance floor,

Bm   D   Em
   Oh I've walked this floor.

Bridge 1

(Em7)
And it gets so hard for me to change you.

                  G   A
Yeah it gets so hard if I change all those things that I do.

Chorus 1

D/F#   G*   A Bm
Same as before, diffe - rent now it's a chore.

       D/F# G*
Don't play a game you'll see that

      A   Bm
You'll leave me wanting more oh oh oh

D/F#   G*   A Bm
Same as be - fore, diffe - rent now it's a chore.

         D/F# G*
Well play a game you'll see that

     A   Bm
You'll leave me want - ing more oh oh oh.

Link 1 ‖: G | Bm | D | Em :‖
w/vocal ad lib.

Verse 2
```
         G            Bm           D
Slave to the game of this in - security,
      Em                        G
A game that's always out to get me
Bm                D    Em
So be here when I get home.
G     Bm                    D
Oh to me it's always been the same,
                  Em                G
You've been a naughty girl going out again,
Bm       D          Em
Oh in the dark again.
```

Bridge 2   As Bridge 1

Chorus 2   As Chorus 1

Outro   ‖: G | Bm | D | Em :‖ *Play 4 times*
             w/vocal ad lib.

             | G | G | G | G ‖

SOFA SONG

Words & Music by
Luke Pritchard, Hugh Harris, Max Rafferty & Paul Garred

(chord diagrams: G#7sus4, B6, E, C#m, F#, B, E, C#, G#5, A, D#m7, G#m7, A6)*

Intro

| G#7sus4 B6 E | (E) | | G#7sus4 B6 E | (E) | |

| G#7sus4 B6 E | (E) | C#m | F# |

Verse 1

G#7sus4   B   E*   B   D#m
The city freeze for   I just realised I don't like you.

G#7sus4   B   E*   B   D#m
Me and my girl   are going out for some air.

G#7sus4   B   E*   B   D#m
And I will do my best,   oh just to get under her dress.

G#7sus4   B   E*   B   D#m
And catch you out if I can on the other side of my sofa.

Chorus 1

G#7sus4 B | F# C#   G#7sus4
           Oh won't you come on over,   at the side of my sofa.

B   F# C#
Oh won't you come on over,   the side of.

Link 1

‖: G#7sus4 | B | E* | B D#m :‖

Verse 2

G#7sus4   B   E*   B   D#m
The city heated up, it got blurry cause I'd had e - nough.

G#7sus4   B
And he tried to take your soul,

           E*   B   D#m
But didn't realise you keep it in a different hole.

Chorus 2

G#7sus4 B | E* B   D#m   G#7sus4
           Oh won't you come on over,   at the side of my sofa

B   E* | B D#m ‖
Oh won't you come on over.

Link 2 | G♯5 | G♯5 | G♯5 | G♯5 ‖

Verse 3
N.C.
So here he comes, a man with a loaded gun,

                                              E   **A**
I don't know if he wants my soul or my   cash flow,

I s'pose I don't know.

Verse 4
G♯7sus4   **D♯m7**   **G♯m7**   **D♯m7**
  So here he comes, a man with a loaded gun,
                   G♯7sus4   **D♯m7**   **E***
I don't know if he wants my girl's heart or her pearls, oh
 A6 | **G♯7sus4** |
I s'pose I don't know
 E | **G♯7sus4** |
I s'pose I don't know
 E | **G♯7sus4** |
I s'pose I don't know
 E | **C♯m** |
I s'pose I don't know
 F♯ | **G♯7sus4** ‖
I s'pose I don't know

SOMETHING TO SAY

Words & Music by
Luke Pritchard, Hugh Harris, Max Rafferty & Paul Garred

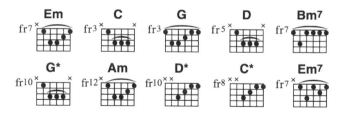

Verse 1

Em   C | G C G D |
Oh lady come on over,

Em   C | G C G D |
Oh won't you please hold my hand.

Em   C | G C G D |
Because nothing seems to work

Em   C
In my head anymore, oh.

   G   C   G   D
I give you one two three four.

Chorus 1

C   Em   C
Because I mean some - thing to say,

        Em   C
Before the feeling goes a - way.

       C   Em
And your out of my life,

C   Em
Oh you jump into his.

Link 1 | Em Bm7 | Em Bm7 | C   G | G C G D ‖

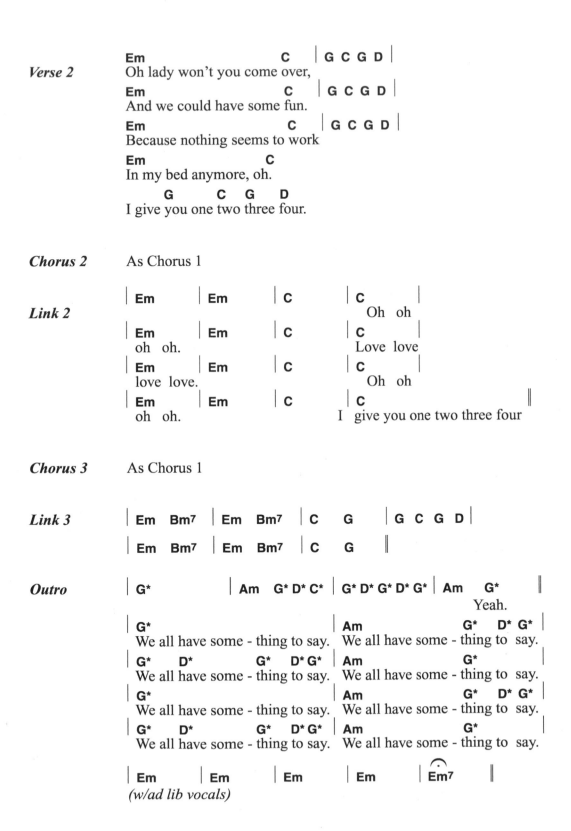

Verse 2

Em   C | G C G D |
Oh lady won't you come over,

Em   C | G C G D |
And we could have some fun.

Em   C | G C G D |
Because nothing seems to work

Em   C
In my bed anymore, oh.

    G   C   G   D
I give you one two three four.

Chorus 2   As Chorus 1

Link 2

Em	Em	C	C
			Oh oh
Em	Em	C	C
oh oh.			Love love
Em	Em	C	C
love love.			Oh oh
Em	Em	C	C ‖
oh oh.			I give you one two three four

Chorus 3   As Chorus 1

Link 3

Em Bm7	Em Bm7	C G	G C G D
Em Bm7	Em Bm7	C G ‖	

Outro

G*	Am G* D* C*	G* D* G* D* G*	Am G* ‖
			Yeah.

G*	Am G* D* G*
We all have some - thing to say.	We all have some - thing to say.

G* D* G* D* G*	Am G*
We all have some - thing to say.	We all have some - thing to say.

G*	Am G* D* G*
We all have some - thing to say.	We all have some - thing to say.

G* D* G* D* G*	Am G*
We all have some - thing to say.	We all have some - thing to say.

| Em | Em | Em | Em | Em7 ‖ |

(w/ad lib vocals)

TEA AND BISCUITS

Words & Music by
Luke Pritchard, Hugh Harris, Max Rafferty, Paul Garred & Peter Denton

A*   G*   F♯m   D   Bm

E/G♯   A   G   A/C♯

*suggested harmony

Intro

‖: *G* | G* | F♯m | A :‖

‖: Bm | E/G♯ | A | G :‖

Verse 1

Bm   A   D   G
I'd like to take you out for tea and for bis - cuits,
Bm   A   D   A/C♯
And show you the city as I see her, how I knew her.
Bm   A   D   G
She is my beauty queen and my lover, yes I love her,
Bm   A   D | A/C♯ ‖
She'll take me to where I want to go.

Chorus 1

G   Bm   A
But out of my blue sky, I see you for who you are.
G   Bm   A   G | G   ‖
But out of my blue sky, I see you for who you are.

Link 1

‖: Bm | A | D | G :‖

Verse 2

Bm   A   D   G
I'd like to take her out for tea, I heard she likes biscuits,
Bm   A   D   A/C♯
Lines on my hands mov - ing now yes they're moving.
Bm   A   D   G
It lets our love be love, but I've got no love to give you,
Bm   A   D | A/C♯ ‖
But still we sit there and I high.

Chorus 2

```
G                       Bm          A
And out of my blue sky, I see her for who   she is.
G                       Bm       A           G   | G    ‖
And out of my blue sky, I see her for who she really is.
```

Link 2   ‖: Bm | A | D | G   :‖ *Play 4 times*

Chorus 3

```
G                       Bm       A
And out of my blue sky, I see her for who she is.
G                       Bm       A           G   | G    ‖
And out of my blue sky, I see her for who she really is.
```

Outro   ‖: Bm | G♯5 | A | G   :‖ *Play 4 times*

‖: Bm | A | D | G   :‖ *Play 4 times*

| ⌢
| Bm   ‖

TIME AWAITS

Words & Music by
Luke Pritchard, Hugh Harris, Max Rafferty & Paul Garred

Chord diagrams: G, D4, F4, Gm/B♭, Dm, C7, D7, G*, Bm, A, Bm, A, Bm*, D, Em7, B♭, D*

Intro

| G D4 F4 D4 Dm Gm/B♭ | G D4 F4 D4 F4 Dm ||
riff 1 _____

Verse 1

w/riff 1 *(x4)*
And time wait for no man, but you.

And time waits for no man, but you.
(C7)   **w/riff 1**
And hoo, don't leave this town.
(D7) (C7)   **G***
And   hoo, don't leave this town.

Link 1

   (G*)   **(G*)**   **(G*)**   **(G*)**
| Bm | A | Bm | A ||
                   riff 2 _____

| Bm | A | Bm | A ||
w/riff 2

Verse 2

Bm*   **D**
There we are,   with that in our hands.
Bm*   **D**
They tear you down,   'cause they don't understand.
Bm*   **D**
You tried it once again,   to love me better.
Bm*   **D**
She tore those panties down,   and loves me wetter.

Chorus 1

```
A    Em7          Bm      B♭     A
  Oh,   oh. And life comes in twos and threes and fours.
G*   Em7          Bm
  Oh,   oh. And I heard you knocking at my door.
```

Link 2

| Bm | A | ‖

Verse 3

```
Bm*                   D
  So hold them down,    with blood on your hands.
Bm*                   D
  It's past the point,    where you don't understand.
Bm*                       D
  The worst you do is lie,    and run for shelter.
Bm*                       D
  So cast these chains,    and love me better.
```

Chorus 2

```
A    Em7          Bm      B♭     A
  Oh,   oh. And life comes in twos and threes and fours.
G*   Em7          Bm
  Oh,   oh. And I heard you knocking at my door.
A    Em7          B       B♭     A
  Oh,   oh. And life comes in twos and threes and fours.
G*   Em7          Bm
  Oh,   oh. And I heard you knocking at my door.
```

Interlude

| Bm | A | Bm | A |

| G* | G* | Bm | Bm | ‖

Outro

```
       Bm
‖: I heard you knocking at my door,
   D*
Darling twenty times or more. :‖ *Play 4 times w/vocal ad lib.*
```

‖: Bm | D* | Bm | D* :‖ *Repeat to fade*

THE WINDOW SONG

Words & Music by
Luke Pritchard, Hugh Harris, Max Rafferty & Paul Garred

A   B7   G#m   E   B

C#m   F#7   F#m   D   B

Capo first fret

Intro

| A | G#m | E | E |

| A | B | E | E |

| A | B | E B | C#m |

| A | B | E | E ‖

Verse 1

A   B   E | E |
I look out of my window,

B   A   E | E |
Oh just to see her arrive.

A   B   E   B   C#m
But she'll be gone, just as soon as I open my eyes.

A   B   E | E ‖
Just as soon as I open my eyes.

Verse 2

A   B   E | E |
And is this a dream, that I'm having?

B   A   E | E |
Oh it all seems so real.

A   B   E   B   C#m
'Cause she'll be gone, just as soon I open my eyes.

A   B   C#m | C#m ‖
Just as soon I open my eyes.

Chorus 1

    A   **C♯m**
And I gave her so very much ,

              F♯
And I never never give enough.

                  F♯m   **B**   **D**   **A**
This love is turning me, into some - thing that I'm not.

                           C♯m
And I've got my problems, yes,

                 F♯
Oh I've got to be the best,

                  F♯m   **B D A** | **A** |
Oh this jealousy is turning me up - side down.

        B7*   **E**
I look out of my window.

YOU DON'T LOVE ME

Words & Music by
Luke Pritchard, Hugh Harris, Max Rafferty & Paul Garred

Am   Dm7   G   C   Bm

E   Em7   A   E7   E7sus4   A/E

G/D   D   C#m   F#m7   B   B*

Verse 1

 Am   Dm7   G
 But you don't love me the way that I love you.

 Am   Dm7   G
 'Cause if you did girl you would not do those things you do.

 Am   Dm7   G
 You kurn my heart just to see if I will rise

 Am   Dm7   G
 Above your anger and above your lies.

 C   G Bm
 And all I see of you, is when you're not so busy.

 G | E | E ‖
 Oh you're not so busy.

Verse 2

 Bm   Em7   A
 And you don't love me the way that I love you.

 Bm   Em7   A
 'Cause if you did girl you would not do the things you do.

 Bm   Em7   A
 You turned my life around and for that I am glad, oh.

 Bm   Em7   A
 However much I love you, this love is getting bad

 Bm   G
 And oh my darling you could chose

 The words that only you could use.

 E7 E7sus4 E7   A G
 But you know you'll always be my girl, oh girl

 Bm
 I'd take you out just for a bite

    G
And show you all the city sights

E⁷   E⁷sus⁴   E⁷   A/E   G/D | G/D ‖
But you know you'll always be my girl,   girl.

Verse 3

Bm   Em⁷   A
But you don't love me the way that   I love you, oh.

Bm   Em⁷   A
'Cause if you did boy you would not   do those things you do.

Bm   Em⁷   A
You kurn my heart just to see if   I will rise, oh

Bm   Em⁷   A
Above your anger and   above your lies.

D   A C♯m
But all I see of you   is when you're not so busy.

A   F♯ | F♯   ‖
Oh you're not so busy,   yeah.

Link 1 | C♯m | C♯m | F♯m⁷ | F♯m⁷ B |

          | C♯m | C♯m | F♯m⁷ | F♯m⁷ B ‖
                            Do, do, do.

Verse 4

C♯m   F♯m⁷   B
You don't love me, you don't care, wo - man.

C♯m   F♯m⁷   B
You don't love me, you don't care, oh wo - man.

C♯m
'Cause you don't love me, you don't care, woman.

(C♯m)   B* | C♯m ‖
But you don't love me, you don't care, wo - man.

Relative Tuning

The guitar can be tuned with the aid of pitch pipes or dedicated electronic guitar tuners which are available through your local music dealer. If you do not have a tuning device, you can use relative tuning. Estimate the pitch of the 6th string as near as possible to E or at least a comfortable pitch (not too high, as you might break other strings in tuning up). Then, while checking the various positions on the diagram, place a finger from your left hand on the:

5th fret of the E or 6th string and **tune the open A** (or 5th string) to the note (A)

5th fret of the A or 5th string and **tune the open D** (or 4th string) to the note (D)

5th fret of the D or 4th string and **tune the open G** (or 3rd string) to the note (G)

4th fret of the G or 3rd string and **tune the open B** (or 2nd string) to the note (B)

5th fret of the B or 2nd string and **tune the open E** (or 1st string) to the note (E)

E	A	D	G	B	E	
or	or	or	or	or	or	**Head**
6th	5th	4th	3rd	2nd	1st	

Nut

1st Fret

2nd Fret

3rd Fret

(B) 4th Fret

(A) (D) (G) (E) 5th Fret

Reading Chord Boxes

Chord boxes are diagrams of the guitar neck viewed head upwards, face on as illustrated. The top horizontal line is the nut, unless a higher fret number is indicated, the others are the frets.

The vertical lines are the strings, starting from E (or 6th) on the left to E (or 1st) on the right.

The black dots indicate where to place your fingers.

Strings marked with an O are played open, not fretted. Strings marked with an X should not be played.

The curved bracket indicates a 'barre' - hold down the strings under the bracket with your first finger, using your other fingers to fret the remaining notes.

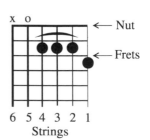

x   o   ← Nut

← Frets

6 5 4 3 2 1
Strings

1 2 3 4 5 6 7 8 9